254

IN MAD WE TRUST!

by SERGIO ARAGONÉS

ALBERT B. FELDSTEIN, Editor

W9-BZR-455

WARNER BOOKS

A Warner Communications Company

WARNER BOOKS EDITION

ISBN: 0-446-88874-5

**Title "MAD" used with permission of its owner,
E.C. Publications, Inc.**

This Warner Books Edition is published by arrangement with
E.C. Publications, Inc.

Warner Books, Inc., 75 Rockefeller Plaza, New York, New York 10019.

A Warner Communications Company

Printed in the United States of America

First Printing: March, 1974

10   9   8

a mi mamá

A HAREBRAINED IDEA

SUBSTITUTE TEACHING

①

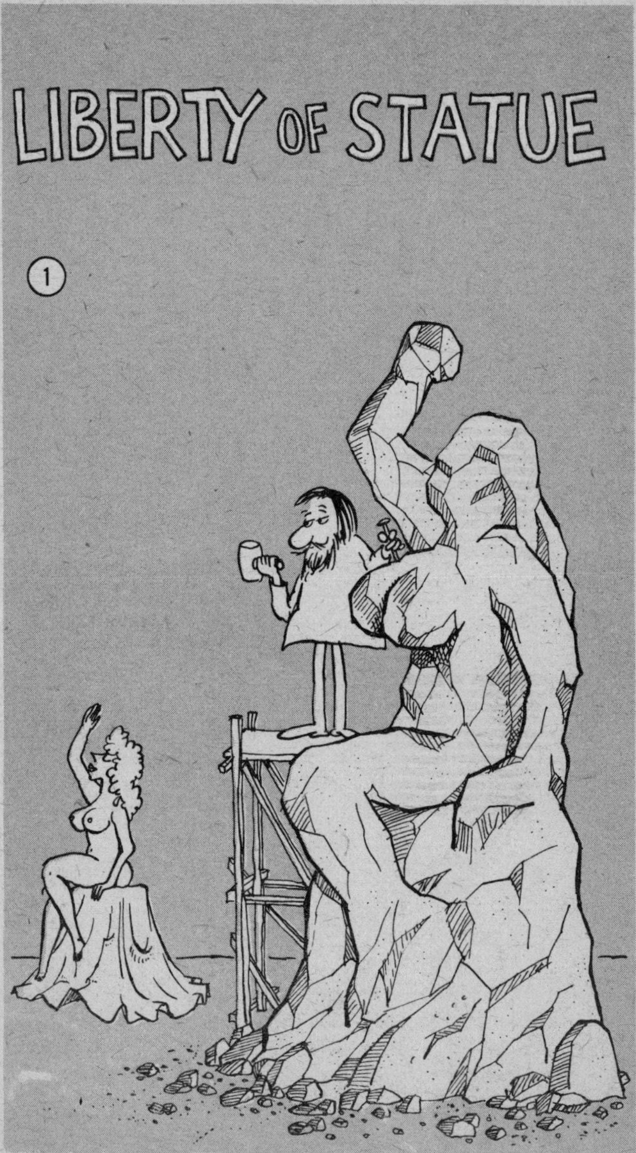
LIBERTY OF STATUE
1

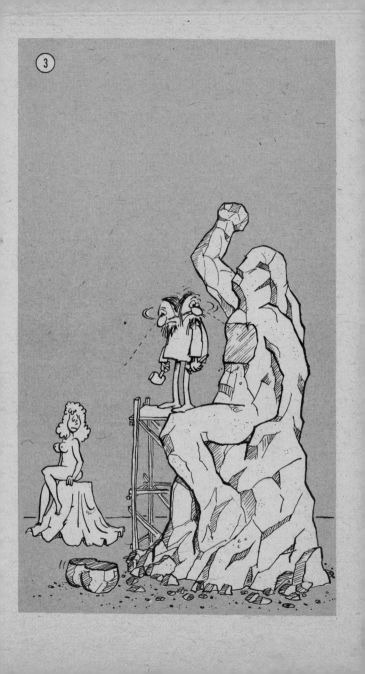

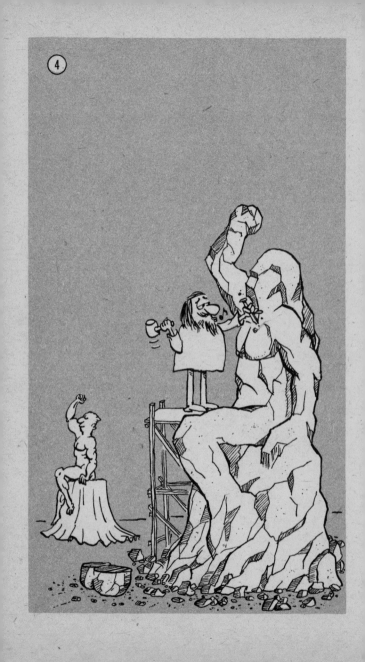

HEX MARKS
THE SPOT

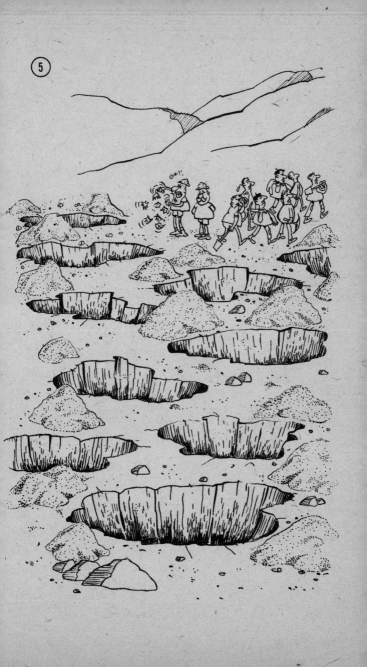

THE TRAVELING BAG

A BALANCED ACCOUNT

ATTENTION, PLEASE!

①

IN QUEST OF THE
HUIZINETZAPOPIXTLAXOCHI IDOL

THE RESOLUTION

①

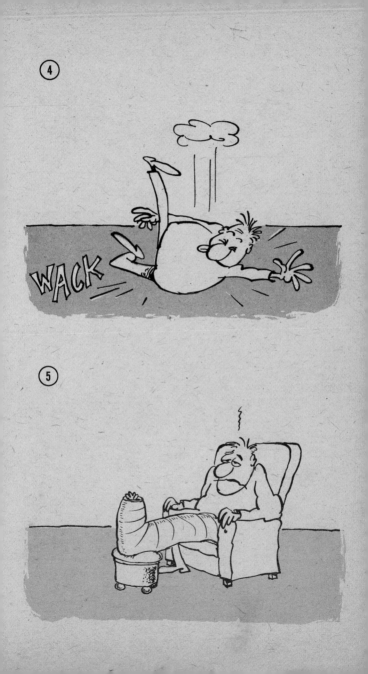

HORSE MANEUVER

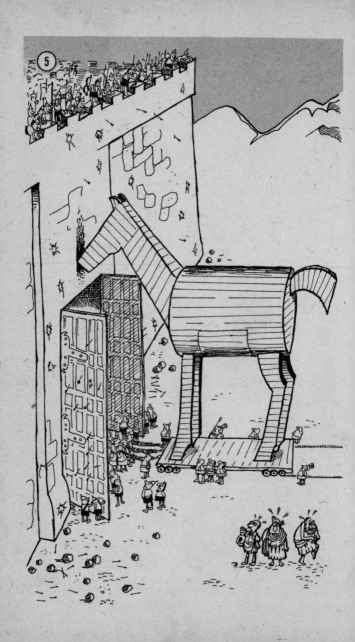

CHILD'S PLAY

THE LAST TANGO IN JERSEY CITY

ONE FOR THE ROAD!

①

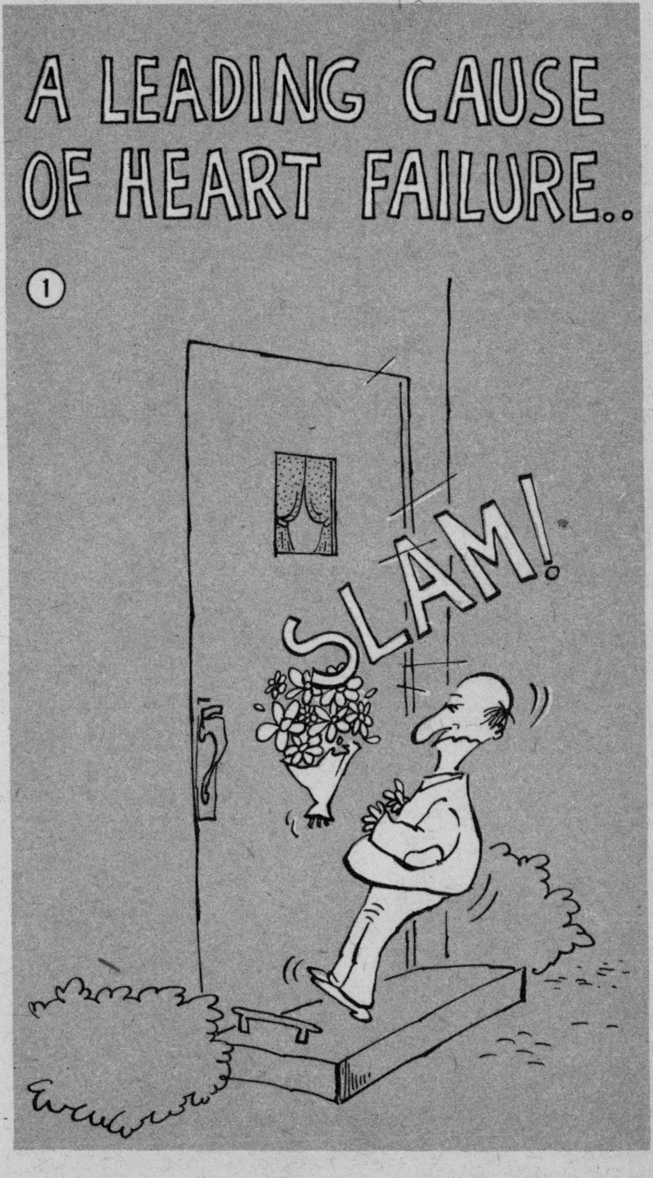
A LEADING CAUSE OF HEART FAILURE..
1
SLAM!

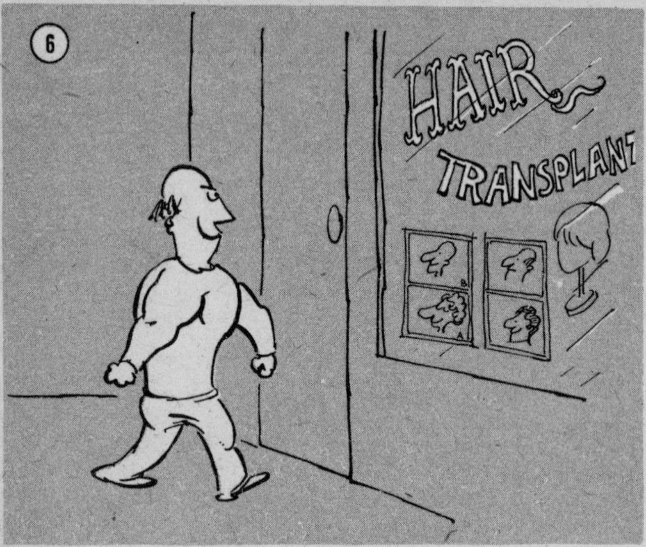
6
HAIR
TRANSPLANT

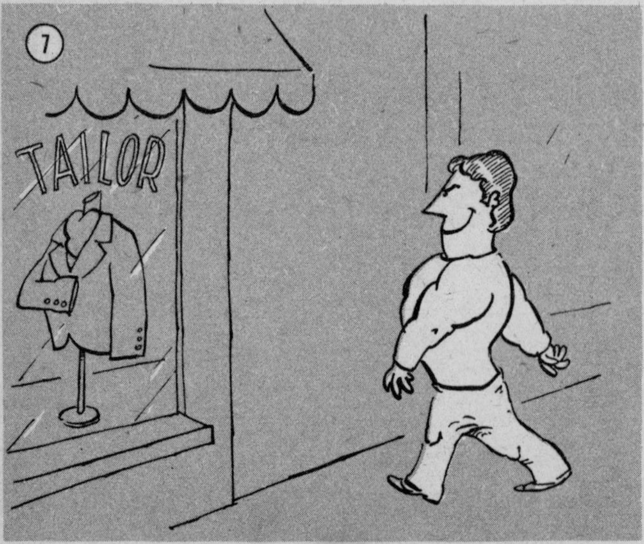
7
TAILOR

A BEASTLY ACT

THE
LAW-ABIDING CITIZEN

SNOW JOB

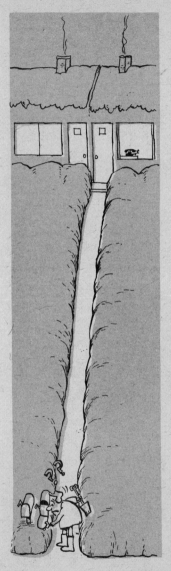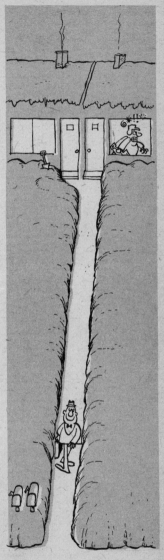

STP ALL OVER THE PLACE!

A GRIZZLY PROPHECY

THE CUSTOMER IS ALWAYS RIGHT!

INDIAN GIVER

ALLEY ALLY

MATERIAL WITNESSES

①

TRAINING AID

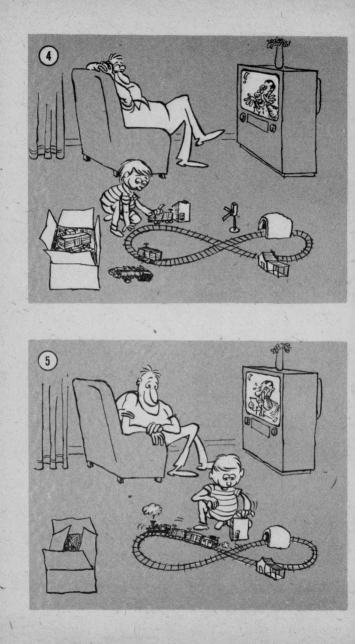

A BURNING SENSATION

CASH ON THE LINE!

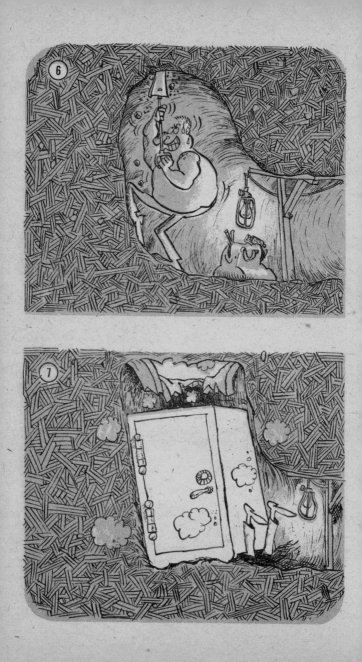

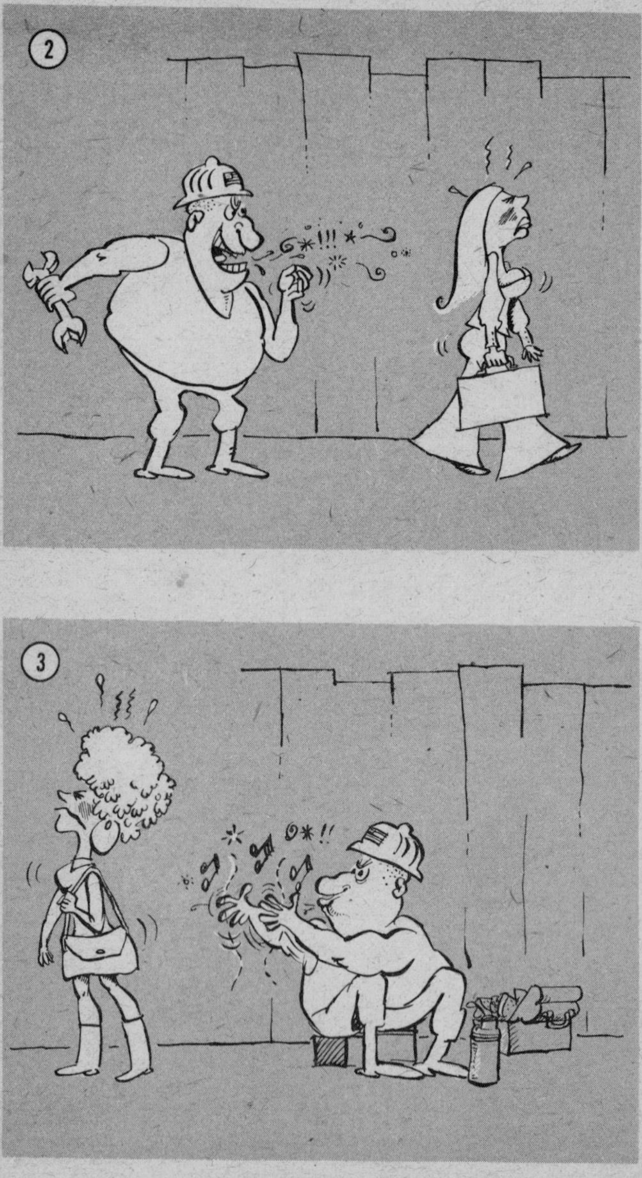
2
3

DIAPER SERVICE

①

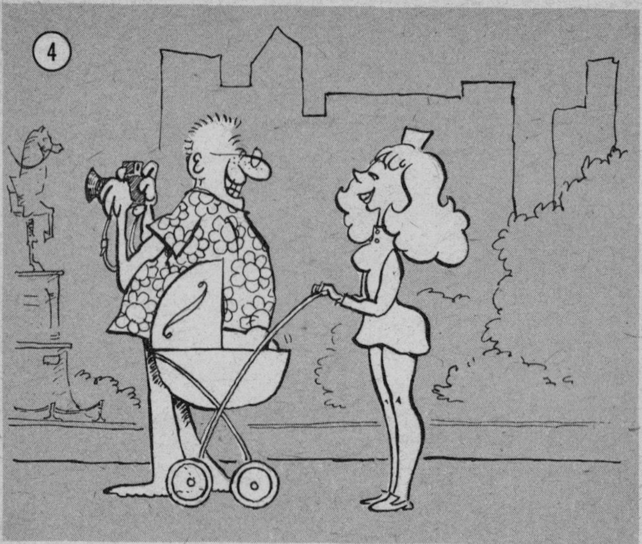
4

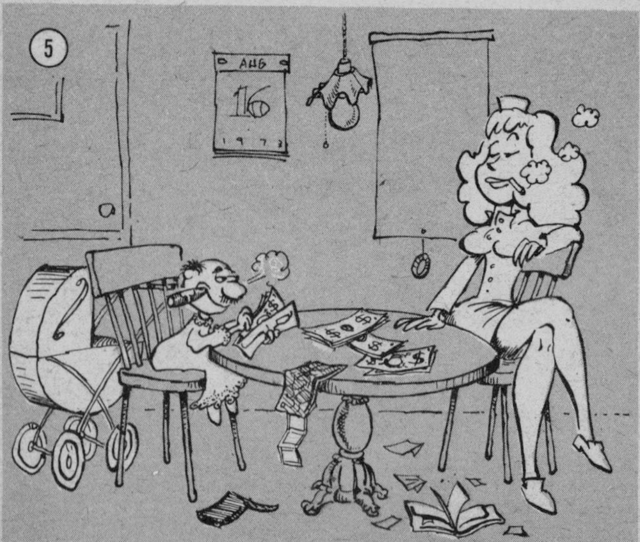
5
AUG
16
1 9 7 3

FIGURE IT OUT!

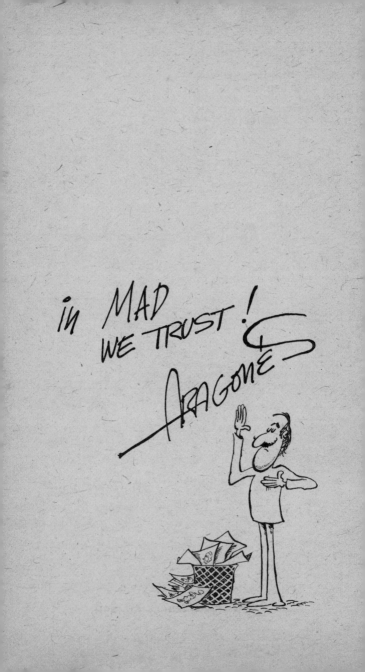